CW00393822

UNLIMIT=D
SONGBOOK

60 SONGS FOR THE CHURCH
WITH FULL SCORES

COPYRIGHT & PHOTOCOPYING

No part of this publication may be reproduced in any form without the permission of the copyright holder of the songs and the publisher of the songbook. Exceptions to this rule are made for holders of licences issued by Christian Copyright Licensing International, as follows:

CHURCH COPYRIGHT LICENCE/COLLECTIVE WORSHIP COPYRIGHT LICENCE:
Churches, schools and organisations holding a church or collective worship copyright licence may reproduce and store the words of the songs within the terms of their licence.

MUSIC REPRODUCTION LICENCE/COLLECTIVE WORSHIP MUSIC REPRODUCTION LICENCE:
Churches, schools and organisations holding a music reproduction licence may photocopy the words and/or music of the songs directly from this publication within the terms of their licence.

For information about these licences visit www.ccli.co.uk.

FOR UK, IRELAND AND EUROPE:
Christian Copyright Licensing International Ltd
Chantry House, 22 Upperton Road, Eastbourne, East Sussex, BN21 1BF
www.ccli.co.uk

FOR USA AND CANADA:
Christian Copyright Licensing Inc,
17201 NE Sacramento Street, Portland, Oregon, 97230 USA
www.ccli.com

FOR BRAZIL:
CCLI LICENCIAMENTO DE DIREITOS AUTORAIS Ltda.
Alameda Rio Negro, 1084 - Sala 75
CEP 06454-000 Barueri, SP Brasil
www.ccli.com.br

FOR ASIA PACIFIC:
Christian Copyright Licensing International
PO Box 6644, Baulkham Hills BC,
NSW 2153 Australia
www.ccli.com.au

FOR AFRICA:
Christian Copyright Licensing Africa (Pty) Ltd,
PO Box 2347, Durbanville 7551, South Africa
www.ccli.co.za

KEEPING WITHIN THE LAW
If your church musicians play direct from hymnbooks, such as this one, then the purchase price of each book pays the royalties due to copyright owners. However, if you wish to photocopy music for your musicians then you will normally need permission from the copyright owner(s). Alternatively you can obtain a Music Reproduction Licence* from CCLI which permits you to photocopy the words and music of hymns and worship songs from authorised** music publications. This licence also permits you to make customised musical arrangements for transposing instruments such as wind and brass provided the melody line remains unchanged.

* The Music Reproduction Licence is supplementary to the Church Copyright Licence, i.e. your church must hold both licences.

** An Authorised book is one which is covered by the Music Reproduction Licence. NB: Both the publication containing the song you wish to photocopy and the song itself must be covered by the Music Reproduction Licence.

For more information, contact CCLI on +44 (0)1323 436103 or visit www.ccli.co.uk.

UNAUTHORISED PHOTOCOPYING IS ILLEGAL and detrimental to the work and ministry of the songwriters and publishers.

All rights reserved. All songs are reproduced by kind permission of the copyright holders – names of which are shown below each song/hymn. Any omission of acknowledgement to composer or publisher will be corrected in future editions.

ACKNOWLEDGEMENTS

Music arrangements and settings: David Ball | david@davidballmusicarranger.com
Artwork: Sublime | wearesublime.com
Executive Producer: Peter Martin

Special thanks to Brenda Cameron and all at Power Music for your help in developing this resource.

Spring Harvest wishes to acknowledge and thank the following people for their help in the compilation and production of this songbook: Denise Anstead, Pete Broadbent, Andrew Crookall, Rachel Gray, Cheryl Jenkinson & Sue Rinaldi.

Published & distributed by Essential Christian, 14 Horsted Square, Uckfield, East Sussex, TN22 1QG, UK. Registered Charity number 1126997.

All Scripture quotations unless indicated otherwise taken from THE HOLY BIBLE, NEW INTERNATIONAL VERSION®, NIV®. Copyright © 1973, 1978, 1984, 2011 by Biblica, Inc.® Used by permission. All rights reserved worldwide.

All copyright details correct at time of going to press.

ISBN 978-1-911237-12-9

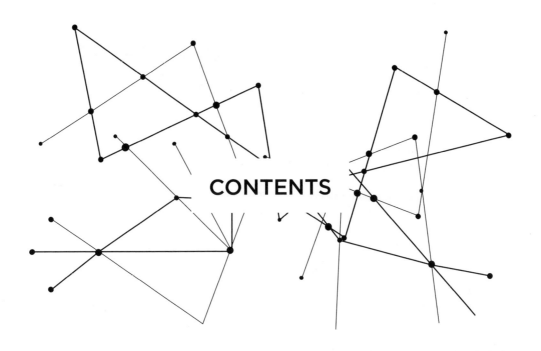

CONTENTS

DISCOVER THE SPRING HARVEST DIGITAL SONGBOOK

Over the years of the Spring Harvest Songbook, we have always been looking at how we can use technology to make worship leaders' lives easier and make the flow of worship smoother. Power Music has been at the heart of our digital songbooks since 2011 and is widely used by worship musicians to free themselves from the hassles of paper music. In Power Music all your music is instantly available on-screen or practice and performance.

Once again we have worked in partnership with Power Music to create a digital version of the Spring Harvest 2019 Songbook. This includes sheet music, chord sheets, lyrics and all the indexing required to find your songs quickly.

Use your iPad, PC, laptop, Windows tablet or Mac as a "digital" music stand to display music or chord sheets on-screen.

WHY USE POWER MUSIC?

- Songs are easy to find by title, first line, category, author and Bible reference

- Quickly set up playlists for your services

- Transpose chord sheets, add capo chords

- Add performance notes

- Link audio tracks for practice or performance.

- Using multiple screens keeps the whole band on the same page

- Synchronised iPad display

- Page turning becomes simple using a foot pedal or by simply tapping a screen or a keyboard.

No more searching for scraps of paper, no more filing song sheets, no more photocopying - Power Music makes worship times stress free for musicians.

UNLIMITED SONGBOOK

iPAD

Get Spring Harvest 2019 Songbook on your iPad using the free Power Music app.

DOWNLOAD* (Windows & mac OS X)

- Display sheet music and chord sheets
- Transpose chord sheets
- Search by title, author, category, Bible reference

Find your unique reference code on the inside front cover

 Windows Mac

HELP*

Getting started

*See inside front cover for details

ALPHABETICAL INDEX

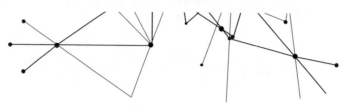

[Song titles differing from first lines are in italics]

essential christian presents | SPRING HARVEST 2019

UNLIMIT≡D

WHEN YOU PRAY...

BE STILL AND KNOW
(BE STILL)

Key = F

Capo 3 (D)

Ben Fielding & Reuben Morgan

Copyright © 2017 Hillsong Music Publishing
publishing@hillsong.com

CCLI# 7102393

BEFORE I SPOKE A WORD, YOU WERE SINGING OVER ME
(RECKLESS LOVE)

Key = Am

Cory Asbury, Caleb Culver & Ran Jackson

1. Be-fore I spoke a word,___ you were sing - ing o - ver me;
2. When I was your foe,___ still your love___ fought___ for me;

you have been so, so good___ to me. Be-fore I took a breath,
you have been so, so good___ to me. When I felt no___

___ you breathed your___ life in me; you have been so, so kind___
worth, you paid it all___ for me; you have been so, so kind___

___ to me. And oh,___ the o - ver-whelm-ing, ne - ver-end-ing,
___ to me.

reck-less love of God.___ Oh,___ it chas-es me down, fights 'til I'm found, leaves___ the nine-ty-nine.

Copyright © 2017 Bethel Music Publishing/Cory Asbury Publishing)/Watershed Publishing Group
(Adm Song Solutions www.songsolutions.org)/Richmond Park Publishing
(Adm by Essential Music Publishing)

CCLI# 7089641

THIS SONG IS
FEATURED ON
**ONLY THE BRAVE
LIVE WORSHIP**

I could-n't earn it, I don't de - serve it, still you give your-self a - way.— Oh,— the

Interlude

o - ver-whelm-ing, ne-ver-end-ing, reck-less love of God.—

D.C. (v.2) *Bridge (1.2. 8vb)*
(Fine)

There's no sha-dow you won't

light up, moun-tain you won't climb up, com-ing af-ter me.— There's no wall you won't

1, 2, 3. *4.* *D.S. al Fine*

kick down, lie you won't tear down, com-ing af - ter me.— And oh,— the

BEHOLD THE KING OF KINGS
(ALMIGHTY)

Key = A

Anna Brading, Simon Brading & Jotham Oakley

Copyright © 2018 Freedom Sounds
(Adm Song Solutions www.songsolutions.org)

CCLI# 7117850

CHRIST BE WITH ME
CHRIST BE WITH ME
(PRAYER OF ST PATRICK)

Key = C

Copyright © 2018 Townend Songs
(Adm Song Solutions www.songsolutions.org)

CCLI# 7118915

essentialchristian.org

NEW SONGS TO RESOURCE THE CHURCH

11 inspirational songs of worship written by a variety of leading songwriters. These new songs are a wonderful resource for churches, worship teams or personal devotion.
All songs are featured in the songbook.

Available at essentialchristian.org/store, iTunes and Christian Bookshops

COME LIKE A FIRE
(REVIVE US (HEAVY RAIN))

Key = G

Luke Hellebronth, Nick Herbert, Brenton Brown,
Tim Hughes, Jimmy James & Willie Weeks

Copyright © 2018 Thankyou Music/Safe & Sound Music/Tim Hughes Designee (Adm. by Capitol CMG Publishing
excl. UK & Europe, adm. by Integrity Music, part of the David C Cook family,
songs@integritymusic.com)/Brenton Brown Designee/Capitol CMG Genesis
(Admin by Capitol CMG Publishing)/Remaining portion unaffiliated

CCLI# 7116247

Bridge

We hear the sound of hea-vy rain, a move of God, the winds of ___ change, your king-dom ___

comes. Your ma-je-sty, a reign of love, an o-pen hea-ven o-ver ___

1.
___ us, your king-dom ___ comes.

2.
___ us, your king-dom comes. Re-vive

D.S. al Coda

Coda

ven. Will you o-pen the flood - gates of hea - ven?

Outro

EVERY EYE IN THIS PLACE IS ON YOU NOW
(EVERY EYE IS ON YOU)

Key = C

Nick & Becky Drake

Copyright © 2018 Worship For Everyone
(Adm Song Solutions www.songsolutions.org)

CCLI# 7117488

THIS SONG IS
FEATURED ON
**NEWSONGS FOR KIDS:
GOD SUIT ON**

you.

Je - sus, you're my joy, you are my free-dom.

Je - sus, you're my joy, you are my free-dom. You're

you are my free - dom.

Photocopy this legally
with an MRL Licence
from ccli.co.uk

FATHER IN HEAVEN
(THE LORD'S PRAYER)

Key = A

Ben Fielding, Benjamin Hastings,
Reuben Morgan & Marty Sampson

Copyright © 2017 Hillsong Music Publishing
publishing@hillsong.com

CCLI# 7102396

FILL THIS HOUSE WITH YOUR GLORY

Key = A

Jafeth Bekx

Verse lyrics:
Fill this house with your glo - ry, fill this house with your glo - ry, let your pre - sence fall up - on us now.

For all things are through you, and all things are to

Copyright © 2017 Integrity Music Europe (adm. by Integrity Music,
part of the David C Cook family, songs@integritymusic.com)

CCLI# 7085283

FOR THE THINGS WE'VE DONE AND LEFT UNDONE
(KYRIE ELEISON)

Key = E

Ted Kim & Cindy Rethmeier

♩ = 66

Verse

1. For the things we've done and left un-done, for the
   i-dols we put on your throne, for the
   lies that we clutch to our chests, for the

ways we've wan-dered from your heart, *Pre-Chorus 1* for-give___ us,___ we pray,
loves we choose a-bove your own, for-give___ us,___ we pray,
fear that wants to steal our breath, *Pre-Chorus 2* for-give___ us,___ we pray,

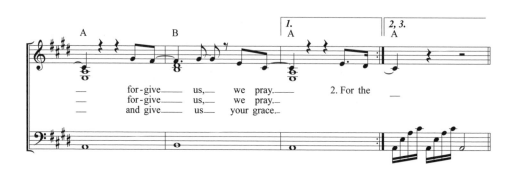

1.
A
for-give___ us,___ we pray.___ 2. For the
for-give___ us,___ we pray.___

2, 3.
A
and give___ us your grace.___

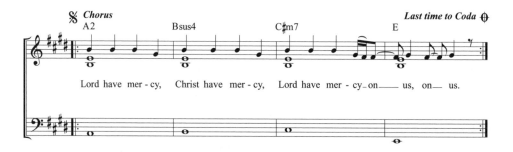

Chorus
Last time to Coda

A2   Bsus4   C#m7   E

Lord have mer-cy, Christ have mer-cy, Lord have mer-cy_on___ us, on__ us.

Copyright © 2017 Mercy/Vineyard Publishing
(Adm Song Solutions www.songsolutions.org)

CCLI# 7086625

3. For the

For-giv-

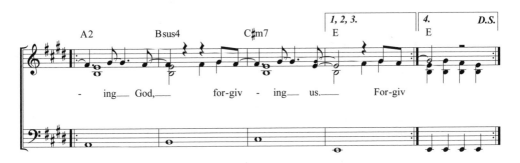

- ing— God,— for-giv - ing— us.— For-giv

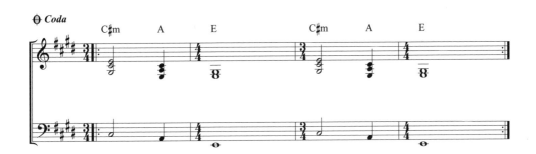

SPRING HARVEST
song search

If you need help to find a song on a particular theme or Scripture passage, or just want to know which of the Spring Harvest songbooks or albums features the song you're after - use our song search.

» search online at **www.springharvest.org/resources/song-search/**

27

FROM THE EARTH TO THE SKY
(HOLY ROAR)

Key = B♭

Capo 3(G)

Jason Ingram, Chris Tomlin & Ed Cash

Copyright © Capitol CMG Paragon/SDG Publishing/Alletrop Music (Admin by Capitol CMG Publishing)/
Fellow Ships Music/So Essential Tunes (Admin. by Essential Music Publishing LLC)

CCLI# 7117455

GATHERED IN YOUR NAME

Key = B♭

Copyright © 2017 Song Solutions
www.songsolutions.org

CCLI# 7093692

31

GOD MOVES IN A
MYSTERIOUS WAY

Key = D

Music by Graham Kendrick.
Words by William Cowper (1731-1800) and Graham Kendrick

1. God moves in a my-ste-rious way, his won-ders to per-form;
2. Deep in un-fa-tho-ma-ble mines of ne-ver fail-ing skill
3. Judge not the Lord by fee-ble sense, but trust him for his grace.

he plants his foot-steps in the sea, and rides up-on the storm.
he trea-sures up his bright de-signs, and works his sov-'reign will.
Be-hind a frown-ing pro-vi-dence he hides a smil-ing face.

1. to v.2 | *2, 3.* **Pre-Chorus**

1. Take cou-rage now you fear-ful saints, the clouds you so much
2. His pur-po-ses will ri-pen fast, un-fold-ing ev-'ry

dread are big with mer-cy and shall break in bless-ings on your head.
hour. The bud may have a bit-ter taste, but sweet will be the flow'r.

Chorus

And I will trust the hands that made the star-ry hea-vens. And I will trust the

Copyright © 2017 Make Way Music
www.grahamkendrick.co.uk

CCLI# 7100920

HE SENT HIS SON TO DIE, AND RISE AGAIN TO SAVE US
(GIVE THANKS TO GOD)

Key = E

Allan McKinlay & Peter Crockett

♪ = 120

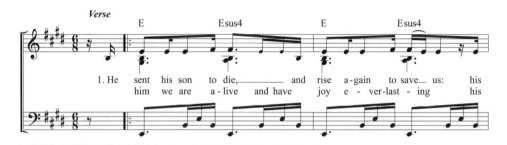

Verse

1. He sent his son to die,_____ and rise a-gain to save__ us: his
   him we are a-live and have joy e-ver-last-ing his

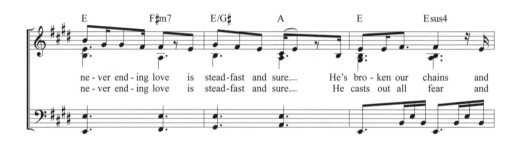

ne-ver end-ing love is stead-fast and sure.__ He's bro-ken our chains and
ne-ver end-ing love is stead-fast and sure.__ He casts out all fear and

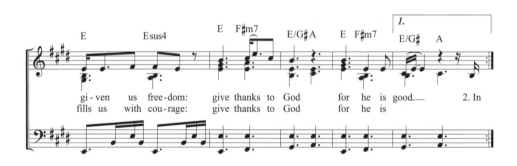

gi-ven us free-dom: give thanks to God for he is good.__ 2. In
fills us with cou-rage: give thanks to God for he is

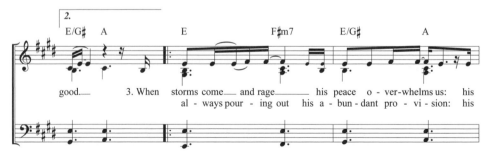

good.__ 3. When storms come__ and rage_____ his peace o-ver-whelms us: his
al-ways pour-ing out his a-bun-dant pro-vi-sion: his

Copyright © 2016 BEC Worship/Allan McKinlay Music Publishing/
Peter Crockett Music Publishing
(Adm Song Solutions www.songsolutions.org)

CCLI# 7065012

HE'S THE LORD OF CREATION
(FILL UP THE SKIES)

Key = C

Andy Baker

1. He's the Lord of Cre-a-tion and the au-thor of light; as he speaks in the dark-ness, he di-
flash-es of light-ning as the rain starts to pour, and the roar of the thun-der is like

vides day and night. There's a hea-ven-ly dis-play of praise and it shines so bright.
praise to our Lord. There's a hea-ven-ly re-sound of praise, can you hear

2. There are it rise? We were made to sing out

praise, we were born to shout God's fame. We are here to lift his name, let our an-thems

fill up the skies, shin-ing like star-light. 1. He's the

Copyright © 2018 Homegrown Worship/Resound Media

CCLI# 7114118

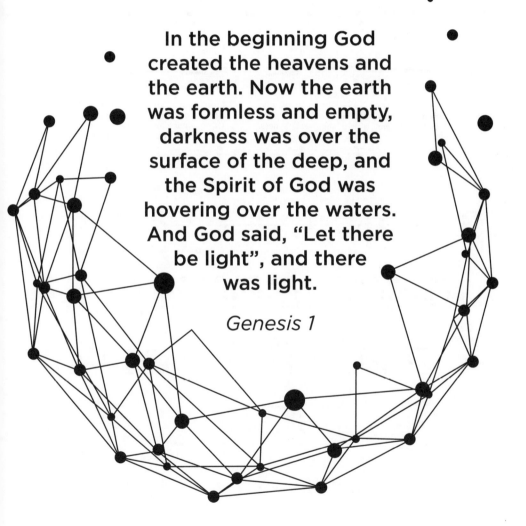

In the beginning God created the heavens and the earth. Now the earth was formless and empty, darkness was over the surface of the deep, and the Spirit of God was hovering over the waters. And God said, "Let there be light", and there was light.

Genesis 1

15

HOLY SPIRIT, GUIDE MY VISION
(HYMN OF THE HOLY SPIRIT)

Key = B♭

Jason Ingram, Chris Tomlin,
Brenton Brown & Pat Barrett

Copyright © SDG Publishing/Vamos Publishing/Brenton Brown Designee/Housefires Sounds/
Capitol CMG Genesis/Capitol CMG Paragon (Admin by Capitol CMG Publishing)

CCLI# 7113814

essentialchristian.org

big start Assemblies

New Resource for Primary School Collective Worship

Deliver engaging, faith-based collective worship for Key Stage 1 & 2, packed full of videos, illustrations, live drama and compelling storytelling. Big Start Assemblies streamlines the planning process with out of the box sessions that are easy to edit and use.

Helping your school meet Ofsted and SIAMS Guidelines

Adaptable - scripts and presentations are fully editable so you can make the content your own

Values based - Themes are built on Christian values including courage, honesty and friendship

Interactive - All sessions include interactive activities and multiple ideas for involving pupils in both the planning and delivery of collective worship

Out of the box - So much more than basic text plans. Everything you need, ready to go

Find out more and start your free trial at
bigstartassemblies.org

HOW GOOD IT IS TO SING
HOW GOOD IT IS TO SING
(PSALM 147)

Key = D

Brenton Brown,
Keith Getty & Stuart Townend

♩ = 86

Verse

1. How good it is to sing, to bring our praise to him whose love and
   fa - mi - lies, or - phans and re - fu - gees, and binds the
   foe can last be - fore his i - cy blast? The winds and

mer - cy knows no end. He brings the sun and rain, he calls each
wounds of those who mourn; the hum - ble lift - ed high, the proud he
waves o - bey his voice. Yet mer - cy will pre - vail, his love will

star by name, the u - ni - verse re - sounds with praise.
casts a - side, his jus - tice faith - ful as the dawn. O shout for
re - con - cile the na - tions of the earth to him.

Chorus

joy to God, and sing a new song, ex - tol the Lord of life for his pro - vi - sion. And he de-

Last time to Coda

lights in those who love and fear him, all those who put their hope in

Copyright © 2018 Townend Songs/Getty Music Publishing (Adm Song Solutions www.songsolutions.org)/
Brenton Brown Publishing Designee/Capitol CMG Genesis (Adm by CapitolCMGPublishing.com)

CCLI# 7118912

HOW GREAT THE CHASM THAT LAY BETWEEN US
(LIVING HOPE)

Key = D

Brian Johnson & Phil Wickham

42

Copyright © 2017 Phil Wickham Music/Simply Global Songs/Sing My Songs/Bethel Music Publishing
(Adm Song Solutions www.songsolutions.org)

CCLI# 7106807

Li - on de-clared 'the grave has no claim on me.' 3. Then came the

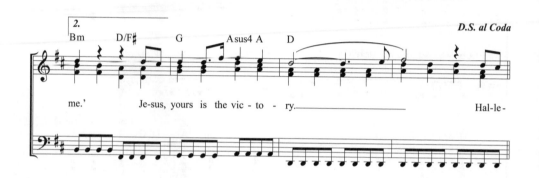

me.' Je-sus, yours is the vic - to - ry. Hal-le-

hope. Je-sus Christ, my liv - ing hope. Oh God you

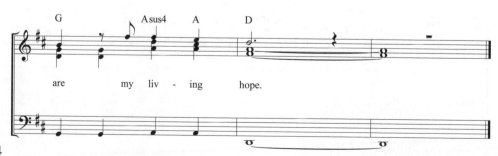

are my liv - ing hope.

essential christian presents | **SPRING HARVEST**

springharvest.org

We need you!

Join our amazing team of volunteers.

Find out about volunteering opportunities at Spring Harvest.

springharvest.org/volunteer

I FEEL IT IN MY BONES, YOU'RE ABOUT TO MOVE
(SPIRIT MOVE)

Key = C

Capo 3 (G)

Amanda Cook, Brian Johnson
& Kalley Heiligenthal

Lyrics under music:

1. I feel it in my bones, you're a-bout to move._____ I
2. I can see it now,_____ your king - dom come;_____

feel it in the wind, you're a-bout to ride in._____ You
I can hear it now,_____ the sounds of Hea - ven._____ You

said that you would pour your Spi - rit out._____ You
said that if we ask,_____ we'll re - ceive;_____

said that you would fall on sons and daugh - ters._____ So like the
we are ask - ing for the great - er mea - sure._____

rain, come, drench us in love,____ and let your glo-ry_ rush_ in like a flood.____
2. pow-er

Copyright © 2015 Bethel Music Publishing
(Adm Song Solutions www.songsolutions.org)

46

CCLI# 7054191

47

I HAVE THIS
CONFIDENCE BECAUSE
(NOT AFRAID)

Key = F#

Mia Fieldes, David Anderson,
Travis Ryan & Adaeze Noelle Azubuike

Copyright © 2017 All Essential Music/Be Essential Songs/Red Rocks Worship/Upside Down Under
(Adm by Essential Music Publishing)/Integrity's Alleluia! Music/
The Worship Society (Adm. by CapitolCMGPublishing.com excl. UK & Europe,
adm. by Integrity Music, part of the David C Cook family, songs@integritymusic.com)

CCLI# 7095716

20

I LOVE YOU LORD, OH YOUR MERCY NEVER FAILS ME
(GOODNESS OF GOD)

Key = A♭

Jenn Johnson, Ed Cash, Jason Ingram,
Ben Fielding & Brian Johnson

Capo 1 (G)

♩ = 63

Verse

1. I love you Lord, oh your mer-cy ne-ver fails me; and all my days I've been held in your hands.

you have led me through the fi-re; in dark-est night, you are close like no o-ther.

From the mo-ment that I wake up, un-til I lay my head, and I will sing of the good-ness of God.

I've known you as a fa-ther, I've known you as a friend; and I have lived in the good-ness of God.

Chorus

'Cause all my life you have been faith-ful, and all my life you have been so

Copyright © 2018 Fellow Ships Music/So Essential Tunes (Adm by Essential Music Publishing)/
SHOUT! Music Publishing (Adm by SHOUT! Music Publishing UK)/Bethel Music Publishing/
Alletrop Music (Admin by Capitol CMG Publishing)

CCLI# 7117726

21

I RAISE A HALLELUJAH
(RAISE A HALLELUJAH)

Key = D♭

Capo 1 (C)

Jonathan David Helser, Melissa Helser,
Molly Skaggs & Jake Stevens

Verse

1a. I raise a hal-le-lu-jah, in the pre-sence of my e-ne-mies,—
raise a hal-le-lu-jah, my— wea-pon is a me-lo-dy,—
raise a hal-le-lu-jah with— ev-'ry-thing in-side of me,—
raise a hal-le-lu-jah in the mid-dle of the my-ste-ry;—

I raise a hal-le-lu-jah,
I raise a hal-le-lu-jah,
I raise a hal-le-lu-jah,
I raise a hal-le-lu-jah,

1.
loud-er than the un-be-lief.
I will watch the dark-ness flee.

1b. I Hea-ven comes to fight for me.

2.
2b. I fear you lost your hold on me.

Chorus
I'm gon-na sing— in the mid-dle of the storm,

loud-er and loud-er you're gon-na hear my prai-ses roar. Up from the ash-es

Copyright © 2018 Bethel Music Publishing
(Adm Song Solutions www.songsolutions.org)

CCLI# 7119315

54

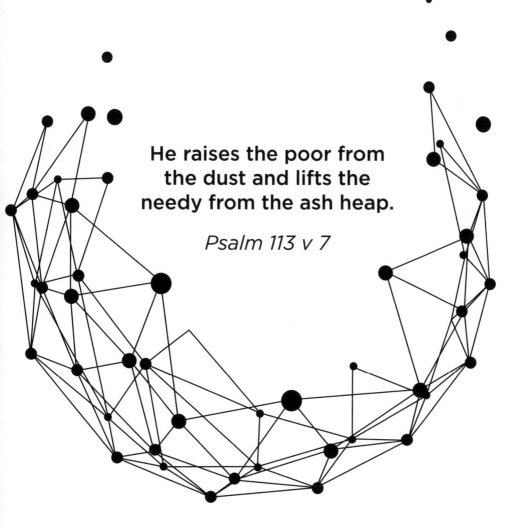

He raises the poor from the dust and lifts the needy from the ash heap.

Psalm 113 v 7

22

I SAW THE LORD

Key = A

Graham Kendrick & Jake Isaac

Copyright © 2018 Make Way Music www.grahamkendrick.co.uk
and Kobalt Music Publishing Ltd

CCLI# 7111046

ho - ly, the whole earth is full of your

glo - ry. I see the Lord, see the Lord, high and lift-ed up;
We see the Lord, see the Lord, high and lift-ed up;

crowned with glo - ry and ho - nour he reigns, high and lift-ed up.
he tas - ted death yet he lives, now he reigns, high and lift-ed up.

ry. I saw the Lord,

I saw the Lord, I saw the Lord, I saw the Lord.

57

23

I WAS BURIED BENEATH
MY SHAME
(GLORIOUS DAY)

Key = D

Jason Ingram, Jonathan Smith,
Kristian Stanfill & Sean Curran

1. I was bu - ried_ be-neath_ my shame;

who could car - ry_ that kind_ of weight?_

it was my tomb 'til I_ met you. I was

breath - ing_ but not_ a - live;_ all my
mer - cy_ has saved_ my soul,_ now your

fail - ures I tried_ to hide,_ it was my tomb
free - dom is all_ that I know;_ the old made new,

Copyright © 2017 sixsteps Music/sixsteps Songs/Worship Together Music/worshiptogether.com songs/
Sean Curran Publishing Designee (Adm. by CapitolCMGPublishing.com excl. UK,
adm. by Integrity Music, part of the David C Cook family, songs@integritymusic.com)/ Fellow Ships Music/
Hickory Bill Doc/So Essential Tunes (Admin by Essential Music Publishing LLC)

CCLI# 7081388

'til I____ met you.
Je - sus, when I____ met you,   You called my
                                                 and you called my

name____   and I ran out of that grave.____   Out of__ the__

dark - ness in - to your glo-ri-ous day.____   You called my name____ and

I ran out of that grave.____   Out of__ the__ dark - ness in - to your glo-ri-ous day.

(Fine)

1.

2. Now your

I need-ed res - cue, my sin was hea - vy,

but chains break at the weight of your glo - ry. I need-ed shel - ter, I was an or - phan,

now you call me a ci-ti-zen of Hea - ven. When I was bro - ken, you were my heal - ing,

now your love is the air that I'm breath - ing. I have a fu - ture, my eyes are o - pen,

'cause when you called my— name,——— I ran out of that— grave.—

Out of——— the—

60

essential christian

essentialchristian.org

NEW BIBLE STUDY RESOURCE

Specially crafted for churches and small groups, this workbook offers a six-session course on Prayer.

Offering both interactive and reflective activities, this course has something for everyone. Each session includes a Bible passage, key thoughts, questions to reflect upon or discuss, action points and prayer guidance.

Available at essentialchristian.org/store and Christian Bookshops

IN THE CRUSHING
(NEW WINE)

Key = B♭

Brooke Ligertwood

Copyright © 2017 Hillsong Music Publishing
publishing@hillsong.com

CCLI# 7102397

IT'S TIME TO DIG A LITTLE DEEPER
(READY FOR YOU)

Key = D♭

Capo 1 (C)

Lou Fellingham,
Nathan Fellingham & Jos Wintermeyer

1. It's time to dig a lit-tle deep-er,
2. You're the wa-ter in the de-sert,
3. We have read a-bout Your king-dom,
4. We're cry-ing out with all cre-a-tion,

to drive a stake in-to the ground; Tak-ing hold of all you've
our sup-ply for ev-'ry need; Ho-ly Spi-rit fall up-
mi-ra-cles we've yet to see; be-liev-ing now for great-er
bring re-vi-val to our land; with gifts of life and re-sto-

pro-mised, we are rea-dy for you.
on us, we are rea-dy for you.
mea-sure, we are rea-dy for you.
ra-tion, we are rea-dy for you.

With

hearts wide o-pen, and hands held high, our faith is

Copyright © 2018 Thankyou Music (Admin by CapitolCMGPublishing.com
excluding the UK & Europe which is admin by Integrity Music,
part of the David C Cook family, songs@integritymusic.com)

CCLI# 7125734

ris - ing, our bat - tle___ cry.

1. Make way for the
2. Sing loud, there's an

King of_ hea - ven, shout loud, let our joy be_ heard; He's
o - pen_ hea - ven, take heart, for the Lord is_ near;_ he's

do - ing some-thing new, our God is on_ the move: he's here,_____ he's here._
do - ing some-thing new, our God is on_ the move, he's here,_____ he's here._

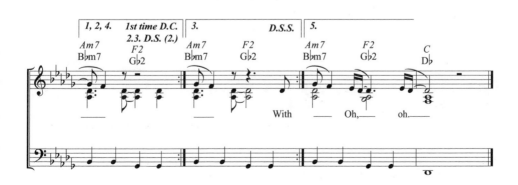

With ___ Oh,___ oh.___

26

LOVE AT CREATION, LOVE AT THE DAWN
(LOVE ALL ALONG)

Key = G

Sam Bailey & Matt Redman

Copyright © Sam Bailey Designee (Admin by Capitol CMG Publishing)/
Matt Redman Designee

CCLI# pending at time of print

THIS SONG IS
FEATURED ON
**NEWSONGS FOR THE
CHURCH 2019**

this is our sto-ry of— hope, all that we lost in the gar - den, for-

e - ver re-stored at the cross.___ Je-sus we come, it was love all a-long._

3. Love on a hill
4. Who e - ver heard

How great, how great is your love.

How great, how great is your love. love.

67

27

MADE IN PERFECT LOVE
(YOUR KINGDOM COME)

Key = B

Pete James
& Harvey Jessop

Capo 4 (G)

Copyright © 2017 Swell Music Publishing
(Adm Song Solutions www.songsolutions.org) & Harvey Jessop

CCLI# 7099497

THIS SONG IS FEATURED ON
ONLY THE BRAVE LIVE WORSHIP
AND **NEWSONGS FOR KIDS:**
GOD SUIT ON

Chorus

Fa-ther in hea-ven, your name is ho-ly; yours is the king-dom, the pow'r and the glo-ry. God of sal-va-tion, un-fold your sto-ry; yours is the king-dom, the pow'r and the

1. glo-ry, a-men. Oh. *(to v.3)*

2. glo-ry, for e-ver and e-ver, a-men. For e-ver, a-men.

NEW STORIES OF WONDERS
(NEW STORIES)

Key = C

London Gatch, Brandon Lake
& Lance Gatch

Copyright © 2018 Songs of BEC/Tilly Tunes
(Adm Song Solutions www.songsolutions.org)

CCLI# 7121992

NO HEIGHT OR DEPTH
CAN SEPARATE
(GOD IS SO GOOD (YOU ARE WORTHY))

Key = A

Pat Barrett, Daniel Bashta & Ben Smith

Copyright © Capitol CMG Genesis/Housefires Sounds/Vamos Publishing (Admin by Capitol CMG Publishing)/
Bread & Wine Sounds/Go Forth Sounds/Heritage Worship Publishing
(Adm Song Solutions www.songsolutions.org)

CCLI# 7100964

Oh,— there's ne - ver been a - ny-one like you,— ne-

- ver been a - ny-one like you, you are wor - thy, you are wor-

- thy. There's ne - - thy.

Photocopy this legally
with an MRL Licence
from ccli.co.uk

30

ON CALVARY'S HILL, IN MORNING LIGHT
(CRUCIFIED)

Key = B♭

Capo 3 (G)

Ian Yates & Stephen Gibson

♩ = 72 **Verse**

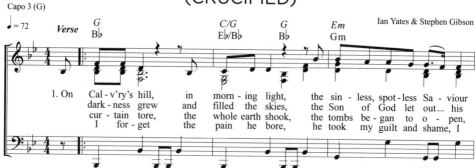

1. On Cal - v'ry's hill, in morn - ing light, the sin - less, spot - less Sa - viour
dark - ness grew and filled the skies, the Son of God let out— his
cur - tain tore, the whole earth shook, the tombs be - gan to o - pen,
I for - get the pain he bore, he took my guilt and shame, I

Last time to Coda

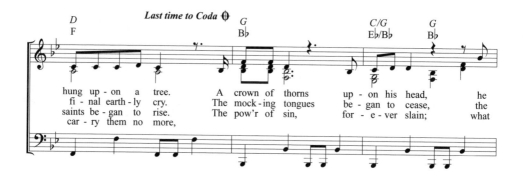

hung up - on a tree. A crown of thorns up - on his head, he
fi - nal earth - ly cry. The mock - ing tongues be - gan to cease, the
saints be - gan to rise. The pow'r of sin, for - e - ver slain; what
car - ry them no more,

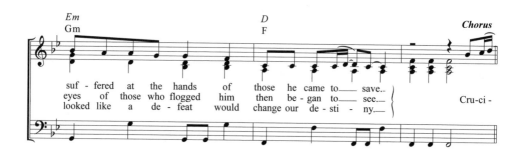

suf - fered at the hands of those he came to— save.—
eyes of those who flogged him then be - gan to— see.—
looked like a de - feat would change our de - sti - ny.—

Chorus Cru - ci -

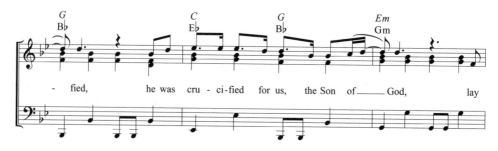

- fied, he was cru - ci - fied for us, the Son of— God, lay

Copyright © 2018 Elim Sound Publishing
(Adm Song Solutions www.songsolutions.org)

CCLI# 7106918

down his earth-ly life. He cried——out, 'It is fi - nished!' O the pow'r, the po-wer of—

1.   **D.C. (v.2)**

— the cross.—   2. As

2, 3.   **(Repeat as required)**   **D.C. (v.3; v.4)**

(The po - wer of—— the cross.)   3. The
                                                 4. Lest

⊕ Coda

I car-ry them—— no more .   I car-ry them—— no more.

31

ONLY YOU CAN MAKE IT
RIGHT AGAIN
(JESUS ONLY YOU)

Key = F

London Gatch, Jesse Reeves
& Aaron Robertson

Copyright © 2017 BEC Worship/Songs of BEC/Tilly Tunes/WriterWrong
(Adm Song Solutions www.songsolutions.org)

CCLI# 7112025

as I can raise them, and I will sing as loud as I can sing.
ther love was great-er, and I be-lieve it's where you made me new.

So let my prais-es be my de-cla-ra-tion: I wor-ship you and you
You are my rock, my hope and my sal-va-tion,

a-lone are King. Hal-le-lu-jah, Je-sus, on-ly you. Hal-le-lu-jah,

Je-sus, on-ly you.

On-ly you can make it right a-gain. On-ly you can make it right a-gain.

PAUSE, BE STILL AND KNOW
(PAUSE)

Key = G

Andy Smith

Copyright © 2019 Song Solutions
www.songsolutions.org

CCLI# 7125790

PRAISE HIM YOU STARS ABOVE
(PRAISE HIM FOREVER)

Key = A

Chris Tomlin, Phil Wickham & Jonathan Smith

1. Praise him,— you stars a - bove, ga - la - xies all in mo - tion;
   beat - ing hearts, sing for— the life he's gi - ven;

praise him, you thun - der - clouds, ring - ing— through - out the hea - vens.
praise him, you res - cued ones, join in— the sound of Hea - ven.

Pre-Chorus

From ev - 'ry moun - tain - top, to ev - 'ry wi - ld o - cean, oh, hear

all the u - ni - verse sing praise. Oh,— sing praise,— let

ev - 'ry - thing— that breathes,— let all the earth— pro - claim:—

Copyright © Phil Wickham Music/Simply Global Songs/Sing My Songs (Adm Song Solutions www.songsolutions.org)/
Capitol CMG Paragon/SDG Publishing (Admin. by Capitol CMG Publishing)/Hickory Bill Doc/
So Essential Tunes (Admin. by Essential Music Publishing LLC)

CCLI# 7117454

THIS SONG IS FEATURED ON **NEWSONGS FOR THE CHURCH 2019**

great is— the Lord our God.— Praise— him for-e-ver, let

all that is— with-in— me mag-ni-fy— his name:—

great is— the Lord our God,— praise— him for-e-ver.

(3°)

1, 3.
A

E

(3°) F♯m7

Last time to Coda ⊕

Praise—him for-e-ver.

D2

D.C. (v.2) *2.*
A

Bridge

2. Praise him— you

Hear the

essentialchristian.org

NEWSONGS FOR KIDS

Especially chosen with kids in mind, 12 totally brilliant songs full of God-truths and enthusiasm to live a life of faith. Written by some of the top children's writers, they are perfect for children and families, and an excellent resource for churches.

Available at essentialchristian.org/store, iTunes and Christian Bookshops

34

PRAISE THE ETERNAL, PRAISE THE IMMORTAL
(HALLELUJAH (LIVES IN ME))

Key = C

Stephen McWhirter,
Matthew Armstrong & Riley Friesen

Copyright © Be Essential Songs/Iron Bell Music (Admin by Essential Music Publishing)/
Friesen House Music/Songs for Full Circle Music (Admin by Kobalt Music Publishing Ltd)

CCLI# 7118745

SPRING HARVEST

NEWSONGS
FOR THE CHURCH
UNLIMITED
2019

THIS SONG IS
FEATURED ON
**NEWSONGS FOR THE
CHURCH 2019**

35

SEE HIM THERE THE GREAT I AM
(BEHOLD THE LAMB)

Key = C

Melodie Malone, Phil Wickham
& Kristian Stanfill

♩ = 75 *Verse*   C   F   Am7

1. See him there, the great I— Am, a crown of— thorns up-on his
   up on Cal-v'ry's— hill, we cursed your— name and e-ven
   up this sa-cri-fice, for ev-'ry— sin our Sa-viour
   age of death is— done, we'll see your— face bright as the—

Gsus4   C/E   F2

— head.   The Fa-ther's heart dis-played for— us;   O
— still   you bore our shame, and paid the— cost;   O
— died.   The Lord of Life can't be con-tained, our
— sun,   we'll bow be-fore the King of— kings;   O

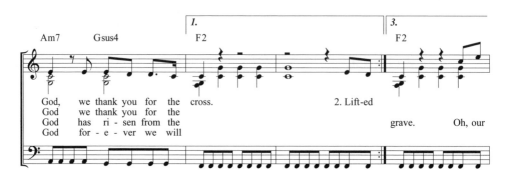

Am7   Gsus4   1. F2   3. F2

God, we thank you for the cross.   2. Lift-ed
God we thank you for the
God has ri-sen from the   grave.   Oh, our
God for-e-ver we will

Jump to Chorus | 2, 4.
Am7   Gsus4   F2   F2   *Chorus*

God has ri-sen from the— grave.   Oh.   Be cross.   1. Be-
                                             sing.

Copyright © 2019 Worship Together Music/sixsteps Songs/sixsteps Music/worshiptogether.com songs/
Kristian Stanfill Publishing Designee (Adm. by CapitolCMGPublishing.com excl. UK & Europe,
adm. by Integrity Music, part of the David C Cook family, songs@integritymusic.com)/
Remaining portion unaffiliated

CCLI# 7122996

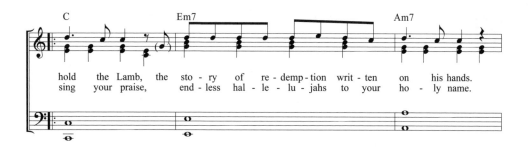

hold the Lamb, the sto - ry of re - demp - tion writ - ten on his hands.
sing your praise, end - less hal - le - lu - jahs to your ho - ly name.

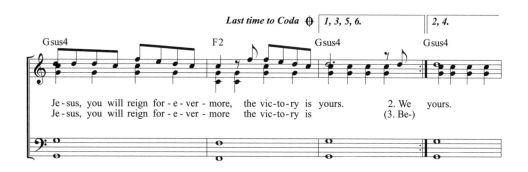

Je - sus, you will reign for - e - ver - more, the vic - to - ry is yours. 2. We yours.
Je - sus, you will reign for - e - ver - more the vic - to - ry is (3. Be-)

3. Of - fer yours. You reign for e - ver - more. The vic - to - ry is
4. When the

yours. King Je - sus reigns for - e - ver - more. The vic - to - ry is yours.

36 SEE JESUS STRIPPED OF MAJESTY
(SEE JESUS STRIPPED OF MAJESTY (AMAZING LOVE))

Key = C

Colin Webster, Phil Moore & Tim Chester

Copyright © 2018 Colin Webster Songs/Phil Moore Songs/Tim Chester Publishing
(Adm Song Solutions www.songsolutions.org)

CCLI# 7117664

SPRING HARVEST

NEWSONGS
FOR THE CHURCH.
UNLIMITED
2019

THIS SONG IS
FEATURED ON
NEWSONGS FOR THE
CHURCH 2019

C *Verse*   G   Am   Dm C/E

5. See Je-sus once a-gain draw breath,   and rise to claim the spoils of death.

F   Am   Gsus4 *Chorus 2*

he sees the light of life a - gain,   and hears his ran-somed peo-ple sing.   O what a

F   G   Am   C/E   Gsus4   Em7

maz - ing   love,   for-e-ver I will praise   the glo-ries of your grace.   What a -

F   G   Am   C/E   *1.*
                                                      Gsus4

maz - ing   love,   I of-fer up my life   a grate-ful sa-cri-fice.   O what a

2.
Gsus4   FG   Am   F   Gsus4   C

fice   for your a - maz - ing   love,   your a - maz - ing love.

89

STANDING IN YOUR LOVE
(NEW)

Key = B♭

Tim Williams & Sam Blake

Copyright © 2018 Elim Sound Publishing
(Adm Song Solutions www.songsolutions.org)

CCLI# 7106923

STIR A PASSION IN MY HEART, GOD

(STIR A PASSION)

Key = C

Josh Gauton, Nick Herbert,
Anna Hellebronth & Willie Weeks

Capo 3 (D)

♩ = 73

Stir a pas-sion in my heart, God, let it o-ver-flow, let it o-ver-flow.

flow. Breathe on___ me, Ho-ly___One, come re-veal your won-der

___now; o-pen___wide my eyes to___see there's so much___more.

Je-sus, you are where it all be-gins; Your beau-ty calls me_deep-er in.

Copyright © 2017 Thankyou Music/Safe & Sound Music/Running Club Songs
(Adm. by CapitolCMGPublishing.com excluding the UK & Europe admin by Integrity Music,
part of the David C Cook family, songs@integritymusic.com/Willie Weeks (Admin by Bespoke Records)

CCLI# 7101548

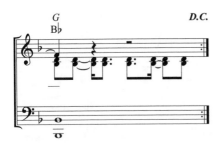

flow.

Let it rise, let it rise; ho - ly fi - re burn in - side.

Let it rise, let it rise; all for Je - sus.

SPRING HARVEST
s♥ng search

If you need help to find a song on a particular theme or Scripture passage, or just want to know which of the Spring Harvest songbooks or albums features the song you're after - use our song search.

» search online at **www.springharvest.org/resources/song-search/**

39

THE GREATEST LOVE SONG, THE GREATEST STORY
(WONDER OF THE CROSS)

Key = B♭

Capo 3 (G)

Lou Fellingham, Nathan Fellingham
& Sam Blake

Copyright © 2018 Thankyou Music (Admin by CapitolCMGPublishing.com
excluding the UK & Europe which is admin by Integrity Music,
part of the David C Cook family, songs@integritymusic.com)

CCLI# 7125739

THIS SONG IS
FEATURED ON
**NEWSONGS FOR THE
CHURCH 2019**

Je - sus pour-ing out_ for us.__ "It is_ fin - ished," in vic-to-ry_ he

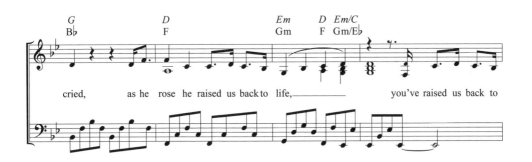

cried, as he rose he raised us back to life,___ you've raised us back to

life,___ 3. Now we're in You've raised us back to life,___
4. Such pre-cious

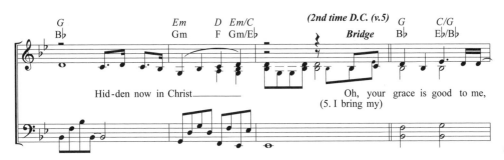

Hid-den now in Christ___ Oh, your grace is good to me,
(5. I bring my)

yes, your grace is good to me.___ Your lov-ing_ kind-ness sets me free,

oh, your grace is good to me.___ Oh, your grace is good to me,

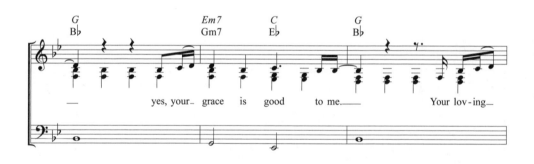

yes, your_ grace is good to me.___ Your lov-ing_

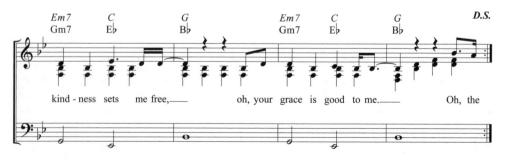

kind-ness sets me free,___ oh, your grace is good to me.___ Oh, the

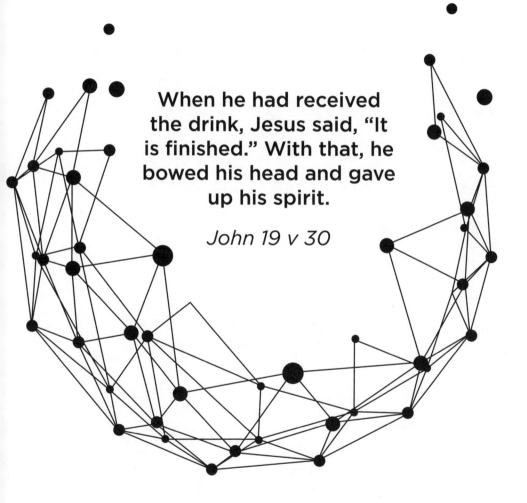

When he had received the drink, Jesus said, "It is finished." With that, he bowed his head and gave up his spirit.

John 19 v 30

THE NIGHT DRAWS IN, THE SILENCE ROARS
(I WILL NOT FEAR)

Key = F

Ian Yates & Sam Blake

Copyright © 2018 Elim Sound Publishing
(Adm Song Solutions www.songsolutions.org)

CCLI# 7106922

99

THE PASSION OF
OUR SAVIOUR
(THE PASSION)

Key = Bm

Scott Ligertwood, Brooke Ligertwood & Chris Davenport

1. The pas - sion of— our Sa - viour,
ty,—

the mer - cy of— our God; the cross—
while the guil - ty one— walks free. Death

— that leaves no ques - tion of the mea - sure of— his love.
— would be— his por - tion, and our por - tion li - ber - ty.—

Our chains— are gone,— our
debt— is paid,— the cross— has— o - ver-thrown—

Copyright © 2017 Hillsong Music Publishing
publishing@hillsong.com

CCLI# 7102399

the grave.___ For Je - sus' blood,___ that sets___ us free,

means death___ to___ death,___ and___ life for___ me.

(to v.2) 3. *D.S.S. al fine* 2.

2. The in - no - cent___ judged guil - me. Means me.

Bridge

I give my whole___ life to ho - nour this love; by the
The sin - ner's Sa - viour, crown him for - e - ver, for the

1, 2, 3. *4.* *D.S.*

Lamb who was slain___ I'm for - gi - ven. ri - sen. Our
Lamb who was slain,___ he is ri - sen.

42

THE ROCKS WILL CRY OUT
(PRAISE IS THE HIGHWAY)

Key = B

Chris Tomlin, Ben Fielding,
Brian Johnson & Sean Feucht

Copyright © 2017 Capitol CMG Paragon/SDG Publishing (Adm. by Capitol CMG Publishing)/
SHOUT! Music Publishing (Adm by SHOUT! Music Publishing UK)/Bethel Music Publishing/
Heritage Worship Publishing (Adm Song Solutions www.songsolutions.org)

CCLI# 7087366

103

THERE IS A SONG, I KNOW IT WELL
(HOPE HAS A NAME)

Key = A

Benjamin Cruse,
Evan John & Ryan Williams

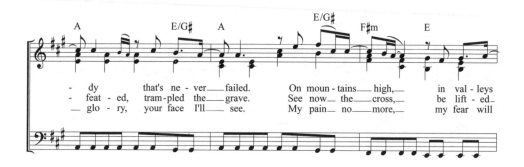

Copyright © 2017 BEC Worship/Songs Of BEC/
River Valley Church Music/River Valley Worship Music
(Adm Song Solutions www.songsolutions.org)

CCLI# 7084823

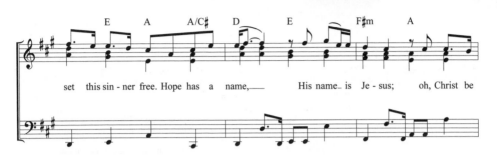

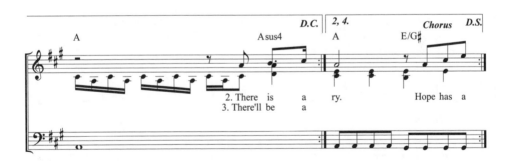

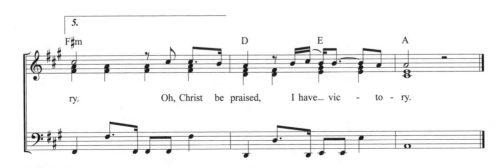

105

44

THERE'S A LIGHT ON
THE HORIZON
(I WILL GO)

Key = F

Lou Fellingham,
Jack Wintermeyer & Jorge Mhondera

Capo 3 (D)

♩ = 108

Verse

1. There's a light on the ho-ri-zon, bring-ing life in-to these
hope that won't be sha-ken, you're the love that won't let
down your life to re-scue, pay-ing ev-'ry debt I
found the great-est trea-sure, the most pre-cious thing to

bones; there's a sound of free-dom ris-ing, stir-ring my heart and soul.
go; you're the song that heals the na-tions, call-ing the bro-ken home.
owe, I sur-ren-der now and fol-low, my life is not my own.
me, now I know there's no-thing bet-ter, I want the world to see,

1, 3.

2, 4.

(2° only)

2. You're the
4. For I've

(4.) Je-sus you're ev-'ry-thing.

Pre-Chorus

I will go ev-'ry-where you go, in your po-wer, we'll see mi-ra-cles.

Won't stay si-lent, I will give my all. (All.) God in your love I'll

Chorus

Copyright © 2018 Thankyou Music (Admin by CapitolCMGPublishing.com excluding the UK & Europe
which is admin by Integrity Music, part of the David C Cook family,
songs@integritymusic.com)/Jorge Mhondera Designee

CCLI# 7125741

45

THERE'S A LIGHT THAT NEVER FADES
(GLORY TO GLORY)

Key = A

Nick Herbert, Jimmy James,
Luke Hellebronth & Tim Hughes

1. There's a light that ne - ver fades:
2. Ev - 'ry - day a mi - ra - cle,
3. Ri - sen with the Son of life,

e - ver bright - er, e - ver true;
walk - ing in the way of grace;
we are changed be - cause of you;

Christ in us a my - ste - ry, hope a - live for all the world to see.
with the sound of hea - ven's roar, call - ing us to live for so much more.
give us faith no walls di - vide, here and now. God let your church a - rise.

From glo - ry to glo - ry,

Copyright © 2017 Thankyou Music/Tim Hughes Designee/Safe and Sound Music
(Adm. by CapitolCMGPublishing.com excl. UK & Europe, adm. by Integrity Music,
part of the David C Cook family, songs@integritymusic.com)/StarRock Music
(Adm Song Solutions www.songsolutions.org)

CCLI# 7101539

greater things are still to come. Our anthem, our story, faithful our God will be.

Last time to Coda

One faith, one hope, one risen Lord; One God who's reigning over all. One over all. From glo-

Coda

109

46

THERE'S A RIVER FLOWING FROM THE MOUNTAIN
(BREATHE)

Key = A

Graham Moore, Jordan Sarmiento,
Whitney Medina & Lauren Evans

1. There's a ri - ver flow-ing from the moun-tain, that shows
our fa - ces shine with won - der, made pure

— our God is true; there's a song ris - ing from the val-
— by per - fect blood; what bet - ter way to give you all the ho-

- ley, it's our re-sponse to you. 'Cause you are God,
- nour, than to bow be - fore the One.

— the God of all cre-a - tion; the earth groans and longs to be with you.

And where we are, our hearts are raised to Hea-ven, we breathe

Copyright © 2017 Influence Music Official/Krispy Music/Sarmo Music/Whitney Medina Music/
Works By Influence Official (Adm Song Solutions www.songsolutions.org)/
Remaining portion is unaffiliated

CCLI# 7087944

THIS SONG IS FEATURED ON **NEWSONGS FOR THE CHURCH 2019**

47

THERE'S BEAUTY IN THIS PLACE
(ABBA FATHER)

Key = D♭

Kees Kraayenoord, Chris Eaton & Abby Eaton

1. There's beau-ty in this place, such beau-ty in this place: your glo-ry shines with-in our hearts. Fa-ther, you are great, we long for your em-brace, your Spi-rit fall-ing o-ver us. And your song of love be-comes our song of wor-ship, with o-pen hands held high

2. Ac-cept-ed and re-newed, now we're one with you through the vic-t'ry of the cross. All hea-ven will re-joice when we hear your voice gent-ly sing-ing o-ver us. And your song of grace be-comes our song of thank-ful-ness; with

Copyright © 2010 Thankyou Music (Adm. by CapitolCMGPublishing.com excl. UK & Europe,
adm. by Integrity Music, part of the David C Cook family, songs@integritymusic.com) /Here's To JO/
West Lodge Music (Admin by BMG Chrysalis US)/Remaining portion unaffiliated

CCLI# 6461793

We're sing-ing, Ab - ba—

Fa - ther, you are here— with us.—— We're your sons and—

daugh - ters. We will ne - ver fall— be-yond—— your love.—

We're sing - ing, ——

113

48

TOO LONG I'VE BEEN LIVING WITH SHAME
(BRING IT ALL TO JESUS)

Key = A♭

Lou Fellingham,
Nathan Fellingham & Junior Garr

Copyright © 2018 Thankyou Music/Running Club Songs (Admin by CapitolCMGPublishing.com
excluding the UK & Europe which is admin by Integrity Music, part of the David C Cook family,
songs@integritymusic.com)

CCLI# 7125737

WE ARE AN ALTAR OF
BROKEN STONES
(HALLELUJAH HERE BELOW)

Key = D

Steven Furtick & Chris Brown

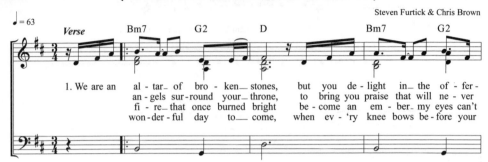

1. We are an al-tar of bro-ken stones, but you de-light in the of-fer-
an-gels sur-round your throne, to bring you praise that will ne-ver
fi-re that once burned bright be-come an em-ber my eyes can't
won-der-ful day to come, when ev-'ry knee bows be-fore your

ing. You have the hea-vens to call your home, but you a-bide in the song we
cease. But 'hal-le-lu-jah' from here be-low is still your fa-vou-rite me-lo-
see, I will re-mem-ber your sa-cri-fice, I will a-bide in your love for
name. But we will not wait un-til it does, for here and now shall your King-dom

1.
2, 3, 4. Chorus

sing.
dy.
me.
reign.

2. Ten thou-sand   We sing, 'Hal-le-lu - jah, hal-le-lu -

Last time to Coda

jah, hal-le-lu - jah.'   We sing, 'Hal-le-lu - jah, hal-le-lu - jah, hal-le-lu - jah.'

Copyright © Elevation Worship Publishing
(Admin by Essential Music Publishing)

CCLI# 7111934

Photocopy this legally
with an MRL Licence
from ccli.co.uk

50

WE ARE GOD'S FAMILY
(HOLD ON)

Key = D

Kees Kraayenoord,
Matthijn Buwalda & Tim Hughes

1. We are God's fa - mi - ly, all sons and daugh - ters, with a hea - ven - ly hope. One day our eyes will see the beau - ty of the Fa - ther's hea - ven - ly home. Hold on,

2. We're bruised yet beau - ti - ful, we are his bro - ken peo - ple bought by his grace. The road is long and hard but God has pro - mised he'll be there all the way. Hold on,

3. The he - roes of our faith, they're all a - round us, and they're cheer - ing us on. So we will not give up, but now pro - claim that in his strength, we are strong. Hold on,

hold on, our God is strong.

Copyright © 2016 Thankyou Music/Tim Hughes Designee (Admin by CapitolCMGPublishing.com
excluding the UK & Europe which is admin by Integrity Music, part of the David C Cook family,
songs@integritymusic.com) /Matthijn Buwalda Designee

CCLI# 7059107

God is for_____ us, God is with_____ us on our jour-

-ney head-ing home._____ He won't leave_____ us, nor for-sake_____ us, we will ne-

-ver be___ a-lone._____ _____ We'll ne - ver be_____ a-lone._____

51

WE CHOOSE TO SERVE YOU
(WE SAY YES)

Key = B

Capo 4 (G)

♩ = 114

Ian Yates, Sam Blake & Joel Pridmore

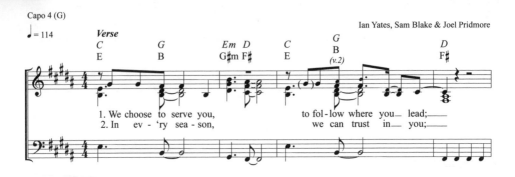

Verse

1. We choose to serve you, to fol-low where you lead;
2. In ev-'ry sea-son, we can trust in you;

to be your wit-ness, to be your hands and feet. We say
for you are with us, you are al - ways good.

Last time to Coda

— yes, my soul says — yes; what - e-ver you have for — me, What-

1, 3, 5. | *2, 4.*

e-ver lies a-head. We say — e-ver lies a-head. We say — yes.

Copyright © 2018 Elim Sound Publishing
(Adm Song Solutions www.songsolutions.org)

CCLI# 7106926

THIS SONG IS
FEATURED ON
**ONLY THE BRAVE
LIVE WORSHIP**

52

WE TAKE YOUR BREAD, WE TAKE YOUR CUP
(CALVARY'S SHADOW)

Key = B

Ryan Williams

Copyright © 2017 BEC Worship/River Valley Church Music
(Adm Song Solutions www.songsolutions.org)

CCLI# 7084831

THIS SONG IS FEATURED ON **NEWSONGS FOR THE CHURCH 2019**

SPRING HARVEST

NEWSONGS FOR THE CHURCH

UNLIMITED 2019

Last time D.S. then to Coda

we stand and tes-ti-fy   that we are   free.

free.

Bridge

No high-er place   than the foot of the cross,—   my sin and shame   o-ver-

come by my Sa-viour's scars.   My Je-sus,   my life, sur-ren-dered to you a-

lone.   lone.   free.

53

WE'RE SEEKING
(HEAR OUR PRAYER)

Key = C

Nick & Becky Drake

Verse

1a. We're seek-ing, we're long-ing, we're ask-ing, Lord of Hea - ven, hear our
1b. We're hun-gry, we're thir-sty, we're cry-ing for a break-through, hear our
2a. O Fa - ther, we're trust-ing, when we don't have the an - swers, hear our
2b. So lead us, com-plete us, oh, will you be the an - chor, hear our

Last time to Coda
2nd time D.C. (v.2)
4th time to Bridge

Chorus (x2)

pray'r.
pray'r.
pray'r.
pray'r.

God, hear our pray'r, hear our pray'r, hear our pray'r

Bridge

O-ver the world,_____ we're sing-ing 'Let your king-dom come.' O-ver the world

D.S. al Coda   Coda

we're sing-ing 'Let your king-dom come.' pray'r._____

Copyright © 2019 Worship For Everyone
(Adm Song Solutions www.songsolutions.org)

CCLI# 7125900

essential christian presents | SONG SOLUTIONS

essentialchristian.org

Copyright and Publishing for Christian Songwriters

Song Solutions is a music publisher and administrator specialising in Christian and Gospel music with over 25 years of experience in handling every aspect of copyright administration worldwide.

WRITERS

Have you written a song for the Church? Find out how we can help.

PUBLISHERS

We can get your songs and catalogues heard worldwide.

LICENSING

Require a license, or not sure which one you need? Get in touch!

Find out more at songsolutions.org or call 01825 748893

WHEN OUR HOMES ARE HIT BY HEARTBREAK
(WORLD NEEDS JESUS)

Key = C

Aaron Johnson, Evan John,
Ryan Williams & Wesley Schrock

Copyright © 2017 BEC Worship/Songs of BEC/River Valley Church Music/River Valley Worship Music
(Adm Song Solutions www.songsolutions.org)

CCLI# 7084830

WHEN WE LEAST EXPECT IT YOU ARRIVE
(COME SURPRISE US)

Key = C

Matthijn Buwalda, Kees Kraayenoord,
Corey Voss & Rhyan Shirley

♩ = 140

1. When we least ex - pect___ it you___ ar - rive, like a wild - fire here in___ our lives.
2. In the mo - ments we're___ not e - ven sure, got no clue of what___ we're wait - ing for.

___ We've got o - pen hearts___ and o - pen minds,___ come and catch us by___
We will trust in what___ you have___ in store,___ as we dare to ask___

Pre-Chorus

___ sur - prise.___ 1. You in - vite___ us in - to my - ste - ry,___ in - to pla -
___ for more.___ 2. You in - vite___ us in___ the hea - ven - lies,___ where our hearts

___ - ces that___ we've ne - ver seen. How we want___ the au - then - ti - ci - ty___ of___ you.
___ - be - hold your ma - je - sty. As an au - di - ence of___ ex - traor - di - na - ry___ things.

Copyright © 2018 Thankyou Music/Integrity's Alleluia! Music/Farren Love & War/Corey Michael Music Publishing/
Integrity's Praise! Music/The Rain Collective Publishing/Rhyan Shirley Pub (Admin by CapitolCMGPublishing.com
excluding the UK & Europe, admin by Integrity Music, part of the David C Cook family,
songs@integritymusic.com)/Matthijn Buwalda Designee

CCLI# 7125786

WHO AM I THAT THE
HIGHEST KING
(WHO YOU SAY I AM)

Key = F♯

Capo 4 (D)

Ben Fielding & Reuben Morgan

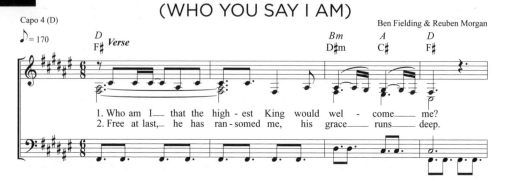

1. Who am I that the high-est King would wel-come me?
2. Free at last, he has ran-somed me, his grace runs deep.

I was lost but he brought me in. Oh, his love for me; oh his
While I was a slave to sin, Je-sus died for me, yes he

love for me. 1. Who the Son sets free, oh, is free in-deed. I'm a
died for me. Fa-ther's house, there's a place for me. I'm a

Last time to Coda ⊕ |1. D.C. (v.2) |2, 4. D.S.

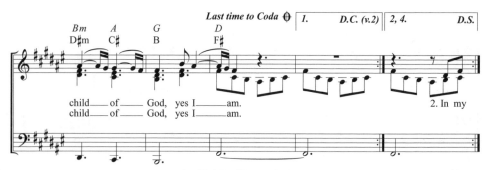

child of God, yes I am.
child of God, yes I am.

2. In my

Copyright © 2017 Hillsong Music Publishing
publishing@hillsong.com

CCLI# 7102401

THIS SONG IS FEATURED ON **NEWSONGS FOR THE CHURCH 2019**

I am cho - sen, not for - sa - ken, I am who you say__ I am.__

__ You are for me, not a - gainst me, I am who you say I am.__ I am

__ I am who you say__ I am.__ Who the

WITH ME, GOD IS WITH ME
(EVERY STEP)

Key = C

Nick & Becky Drake

♩ = 120

Verse

1. With me, God is with me, yes, he's with me ev-'ry step.
2. With you God is with you, yes, he's with you ev-'ry step.
3. With us, God is with us, yes, he's with us ev-'ry step.

Repeat each verse

me ev-'ry step.
you ev-'ry step.
us ev-'ry step.

Pre-Chorus

1. And I know God is with me ev-'ry step
2. And I know God is with you ev-'ry step
3. And I know God is with us ev-'ry step

— I go; I know God is with me ev-'ry step.
— you go; I know God is with you ev-'ry step.
— we go; I know God is with us ev-'ry step.

D.C. (v.2)

Chorus

And oh, the love of God is
— will lead me on, in-

Copyright © 2018 Worship For Everyone
(Adm Song Solutions www.songsolutions.org)

CCLI# 7122275

THIS SONG IS FEATURED ON NEWSONGS FOR KIDS: GOD SUIT ON

with me ev - 'ry day,___ ev - 'ry step I take.___ He
to his per - fect plan,___ walk-ing hand in hand.___

Ev - 'ry step.___ Ev - 'ry step..

Ev - 'ry step.___

SPRING HARVEST song search

If you need help to find a song on a particular theme or Scripture passage, or just want to know which of the Spring Harvest songbooks or albums features the song you're after - use our song search.

» search online at **www.springharvest.org/resources/song-search/**

58

YOU ARE THE ONE WHO WILL PROVIDE
(COMPANION)

Key = F

David Lyon & Allan McKinlay

Copyright © 2018 Daybreak/Allan McKinlay Music Publishing
(Adm Song Solutions www.songsolutions.org)

CCLI# 7112547

THIS SONG IS FEATURED ON **NEWSONGS FOR THE CHURCH 2019**

2. You are the com- need. There is no need.

In the pre - sence of my— e - ne - mies,
I will ne - ver— be a - lone, for

you will make a way for me, a hid - ing place where— bless-ing o - ver-
love and good - ness lead me on, and in your house for-

flows. And e - ver I will dwell. There is no

need, you're the com - pa - nion in my need.

YOU HAVE SHOWN ME GRACE
(ENDLESS PRAISES)

Key = Em

Dave Miller, James Melachrino,
Phil Clay & Stephen Peter Rowe

Copyright © 2018 Vineyard Songs (UK/Eire)
(Adm Song Solutions www.songsolutions.org)

CCLI# 7116755

137

YOUR GREAT LOVE BURNS
WITHIN OUR HEARTS
(YOU ARE WORTHY)

Key = D

Becky Frith

1. Your great love burns with-in our hearts; when you speak, light dis-pels the
   rise, kings and ru-lers fall, yet you are sov-'reign o-ver
   seems dark-ness will pre-vail, we have hope: your love ne-ver

dark. We be-lieve in your re-deem-ing pow'r, and you are mak-ing all things
all. You are Lord, and one day all will come and bow be-fore your ho-ly
fails. We are yours, our des-ti-ny as-sured; we'll live with you for-e-ver-

new.
throne. You are wor-thy, so wor-thy, King Je-sus, Lord of all. You are
more.

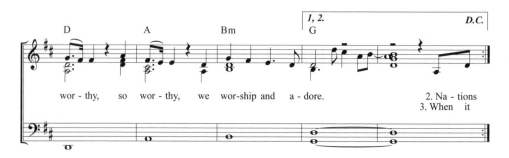

wor-thy, so wor-thy, we wor-ship and a-dore.

2. Na-tions
3. When it

Copyright © 2018 Song Solutions
www.songsolutions.org

CCLI# 7105858

THIS SONG IS FEATURED ON **NEWSONGS FOR THE CHURCH 2019**

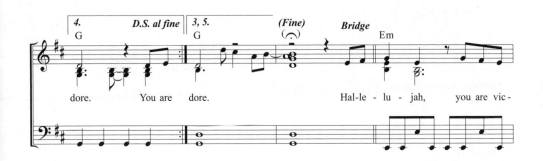

dore.   You are   dore.   Hal-le - lu - jah,   you are vic-

to - ri - ous. Hal-le - lu - jah,   for-e-ver glo - ri - ous. Hal-le - lu - jah,   we are a-

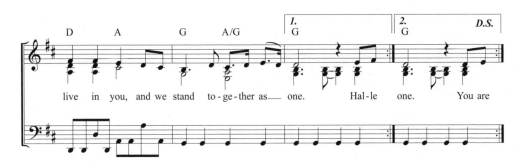

live in you, and we stand to-ge-ther as— one.   Hal-le one.   You are

Photocopy this legally with an MRL Licence from ccli.co.uk

Experts In Event Solutions

EVENT MANAGEMENT

TICKETING

DELEGATE REGISTRATION

EXHIBITION PLANNING AND MANAGEMENT

HEALTH & SAFETY

TECHNICAL MANAGEMENT

RECORDING &

BRIDGES TO C

BRIDGES TO D

BRIDGES TO E

BRIDGES TO F

BRIDGES TO G

GUITAR CHORDS

A good chord vocabulary is essential for a guitarist to feel confident when playing in worship, especially when the situation may involve reading a previously unseen piece of music or picking up a song quickly by ear. The chords on these pages are arranged in 'families' according to key.

This is a beneficial way of remembering chords as most songs stick to these groupings. For each key, the first row shows the simplest form of each chord and the second line gives a more interesting substitution. The third line shows the chords most commonly used by guitarists derived by keeping some sort of pedal tone ringing in each chord and the fourth line shows inverted chords with an alternate bass note.

Also included are the Roman Numerals and Nashville Numbers associated with each chord. If you've not come across these before, they are simply an easy way of numbering each chord within a key. This is useful as it means you can take any chord progression in one key and instantly transpose it to another. Furthermore you can try out any of the chords in each column that corresponds to the relevant Roman Numeral and see if there is chord type or inversion which still fits but adds a different flavour. Experimentation like this may open up creative chord progressions that serve as a catalyst to help you to worship in fresh ways or to write new songs.

Roman	I	II	III	IV	V	VI	VII
Nashville	1	2	3	4	5	6	7
Key of C — 3-note chord (triad)	C	Dm	Em	F	G	Am	Bdim
4-note chord	C maj7	D m7	E m7	F maj7	G7	A m7	B m7♭5
Alternative substitute	C	D7sus4	E m7	F sus2	G5	A m7	Dsus4/B
Alternative bass note	C/E	Dm/F	Em/G	F/A	F/G	Am/E	

For all chords in the key of C# or Db, use the chords from the key of C with capo 1

146

GUITAR CHORDS

Key of D

Roman	I	II	III	IV	V	VI	VII
Nashville	1	2	3	4	5	6	7
3-note chord (triad)	D	Em	F#m	G	A	Bm	C#dim
4-note chord	Dmaj7	Em7	F#m7	Gmaj7	A7	Bm7	C#m7♭5
Alternative substitute	Dsus2	Em9	F#m7	G6sus2	A7sus4	Bm11	Aadd9/C#
Alternative bass note	D/F#	Em/B	F#m/A	G/B	G/A	Bm/F#	

For all chords in the key of D# or E♭, use the chords from the key of D with capo 1

Key of E

3-note chord (triad)	E	F#m	G#m	A	B	C#m	D#dim
4-note chord	Emaj7	F#m7	G#m7	Amaj7	B7	C#m7	D#m7♭5
Alternative substitute	E5	F#m11	G#madd♭6	Aadd9	Badd4	C#m7	D#alt
Alternative bass note	E/G#	F#m/C#	G#m/D#	A/C#	A/B	C#m/G#	

For all chords in the key of F, use the chords from the key of E with capo 1

For all chords in the key of F# or Gb, use the chords from the key of E with capo 2

GUITAR CHORDS

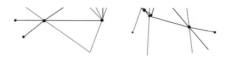

	Roman	I	II	III	IV	V	VI	VII
	Nashville	1	2	3	4	5	6	7
Key of G	3-note chord (triad)	G	Am	Bm	C	D	Em	F#dim
	4-note chord	Gmaj7	Am7	Bm7	Cmaj7	D7	Em7	F#m7♭5
	Alternative substitute	G	A7sus4	Dsus4/B	Cadd9	Dsus4	Em7	G/F#
	Alternative bass note	G/D	Am/C	Bm/D	C/G	C/D	Em/G	

For all chords in the key of G# or A♭, use the chords from the key of G with capo 1

	Roman	I	II	III	IV	V	VI	VII
Key of A	3-note chord (Triad)	A	Bm	C#m	D	E	F#m	G#dim
	4-note chord	Amaj7	Bm7	C#m7	Dmaj7	E7	F#m7	G#m7♭5
	Alternative substitute	Asus2	Bsus4	C#m7	D6sus2	Eadd9	F#m11	Eadd9/G#
	Alternative bass note	A/E	Bm/F#	C#m/E	D/A	D/E	F#m/A	

For all chords in the key of A# or Bb, use the chords from the key of A with capo 1

For all chords in the key of B, use the chords from the key of A with capo 2

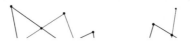

SCRIPTURE INDEX

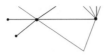

JOHN

1:3-5	There's a light that never fades
1:5	Your great love burns within our hearts
1:12	Who am I that the highest King
1:16	The greatest love song, the greatest story
1:29	See him there the great I am
3:16	Love at creation, love at the dawn
4:13	There's a river flowing from the mountain
6:20	Too long I've been living with shame
8:12	Praise the eternal, praise the immortal
8:36	There's a light on the horizon
8:36	Who am I that the highest King
9:5	Praise the eternal, praise the immortal
11:38-44	I was buried beneath my shame
14:12	There's a light that never fades
14:16	We are God's family
15:13	Only you can make it right again
16:13	Holy Spirit, guide my vision
16:33	Every eye in this place is on you now
19:2	On Calvary's hill, in morning light
19:2	See him there the great I am
19:30	On Calvary's hill, in morning light
19:30	The greatest love song, the greatest story
20:22	Stir a passion in my heart, God

ACTS

1:8	New stories of wonders
2:1-3	Come like a fire
2:25	I have this confidence because
2:25	There's a light on the horizon
3:21	It's time to dig a little deeper
8:32	See Jesus stripped of majesty
13:47	When our homes are hit by heartbreak
17:28	He sent his Son to die, and rise again to save us

ROMANS

3:24	Who am I that the highest King
6:8	We take your bread, we take your cup
6:8	When our homes are hit by heartbreak
8:15	There's beauty in this place
8:26	There's a river flowing from the mountain
8:31	We choose to serve you
8:31	Who am I that the highest King
8:34	The passion of our Saviour
8:38	Before I spoke a word, you were singing over me
8:39	No height or depth can separate
12:1	See Jesus stripped of majesty
12:11	We choose to serve you
13:14	Christ be with me
14:11	We are an altar of broken stones
15:19	New stories of wonders

1 CORINTHIANS

11:26	We take your bread, we take your cup
13:8	Your great love burns within our hearts
13:12	We are God's family
15:54	The passion of our Saviour
15:54	We take your bread, we take your cup
15:54	You have shown me grace
15:57	There is a song, I know it well
15:57	There's beauty in this place

2 CORINTHIANS

4:9	With me, God is with me
5:17-19	No height or depth can separate
5:19	For the things we've done and left undone
9:8	You are the One who will provide
12:12	New stories of wonders
13:14	The greatest love song, the greatest story

GALATIANS

3:26	We are God's family
4:6	There's beauty in this place
5:1	How great the chasm that lay between us
5:1	Standing in your love
6:18	Christ be with me

EPHESIANS

1:7	How great the chasm that lay between us
1:7	Standing in your love
2:4	See Jesus stripped of majesty
2:8	You have shown me grace
2:16	The greatest love song, the greatest story
2:19	We are God's family
2:22	Praise the eternal, praise the immortal
2:1-10	I was buried beneath my shame
2:4-5	Love at creation, love at the dawn
3:12	I have this confidence because

PHILIPPIANS

2:10	Behold the King of kings
2:10	We are an altar of broken stones
4:19	Too long I've been living with shame
4:23	Christ be with me

COLOSSIANS

2:15	The greatest love song, the greatest story

1 THESSALONIANS

5:28	Christ be with me

2 THESSALONIANS

2:16	You have shown me grace
3:8	Christ be with me

1 TIMOTHY

1:17	Praise the eternal, praise the immortal
6:13	Only you can make it right again
6:15	Behold the King of kings
6:15	Fill this house with your glory
6:15	God moves in a mysterious way
6:16	Praise the eternal, praise the immortal

2 TIMOTHY

1:6	Stir a passion in my heart, God
1:10	I raise a hallelujah
1:10	The greatest love song, the greatest story
2:21	In the crushing
4:22	It's time to dig a little deeper

TITUS

2:11	The greatest love song, the greatest story
3:4	How great the chasm that lay between us
3:4	The greatest love song, the greatest story

PHILEMON

6	It's time to dig a little deeper
25	Christ be with me

HEBREWS

2:4	New stories of wonders
2:7	I saw the Lord
6:19	We're seeking
9:14	We choose to serve you
12:2	The greatest love song, the greatest story
13:5	We are God's family
13:6	I have this confidence because
13:9	You have shown me grace

1 PETER

1:3	How great the chasm that lay between us
2:4	We are an altar of broken stones
2:25	Made in perfect love
5:6	When our homes are hit by heartbreak

2 PETER

1:16	When we least expect it you arrive

1 JOHN

2:2	See Jesus stripped of majesty
4:10	He sent his Son to die, and rise again to save us
4:10	See Jesus stripped of majesty
4:18	Be still and know
4:18	Made in perfect love
5:1	When our homes are hit by heartbreak

JUDE

21	Pause, be still and know

REVELATION

1:5	How great the chasm that lay between us
1:5	Standing in your love
1:7	Every eye in this place is on you now
1:16	There's a river flowing from the mountain
1:17	Too long I've been living with shame
3:3	When we least expect it you arrive
4:1-8	I saw the Lord
4:8	Fill this house with your glory
4:10	Behold the King of kings
4:10-11	Your great love burns within our hearts
4:11	From the earth to the sky
5:11	We are an altar of broken stones
5:12	From the earth to the sky
5:12	The passion of our Saviour
5:12	Your great love burns within our hearts
7:17	Behold the King of kings
11:19	He's the Lord of creation
12:12	There's beauty in this place
17:14	Behold the King of kings
19:1	I raise a hallelujah
19:1	Praise the eternal, praise the immortal
19:1	We are an altar of broken stones
19:1	We choose to serve you
19:1	You have shown me grace
19:1	Your great love burns within our hearts
19:16	Behold the King of kings
19:16	Fill this house with your glory
21:4	There is a song, I know it well
21:5	Standing in your love
21:5	When we least expect it you arrive
21:5	Your great love burns within our hearts
22:3	Behold the King of kings
22:4	Gathered in your name
22:4	We are God's family
22:20	Come like a fire
22:20	New stories of wonders

THEMATIC INDEX

CALL TO WORSHIP

Every eye in this place is on you now

Fill this house with your glory

From the earth to the sky

Gathered in your name

He's the Lord of creation

How good it is to sing

Praise him you stars above

The rocks will cry out

We are an altar of broken stones

Who am I that the highest King

THE CHURCH, THE PEOPLE OF GOD

Gathered in your name

How good it is to sing

The rocks will cry out

There's a light that never fades

There's beauty in this place

We are an altar of broken stones

We are God's family

When our homes are hit by heartbreak

COME LORD JESUS - THE PRESENCE OF GOD

Be still and know

Come like a fire

Fill this house with your glory

I feel it in my bones, you're about to move

It's time to dig a little deeper

New stories of wonders

Pause, be still and know

We're seeking

When we least expect it you arrive

You are the One who will provide

COMMUNION
(SEE ALSO JESUS - CROSS AND RESURRECTION)

On Calvary's hill, in morning light

See him there the great I am

See Jesus stripped of majesty

The greatest love song, the greatest story

We take your bread, we take your cup

CONFESSION

Father in Heaven

For the things we've done and left undone

I saw the Lord

I was buried beneath my shame

Made in perfect love

See him there the great I am

The greatest love song, the greatest story

The passion of our Saviour

Too long I've been living with shame

Who am I that the highest King

CREATION

Behold the King of kings

He's the Lord of creation

How good it is to sing

Praise him you stars above

The rocks will cry out

There's a river flowing from the mountain

DEDICATION AND COMMITMENT

How great the chasm that lay between us

I love you Lord, oh your mercy never fails me

In the crushing

See Jesus stripped of majesty

Stir a passion in my heart, God

The passion of our Saviour

There's a light on the horizon

We choose to serve you

When our homes are hit by heartbreak

FAITH AND TRUST

Be still and know

God moves in a mysterious way

Holy Spirit, guide my vision

I have this confidence because

In the crushing

New stories of wonders

No height or depth can separate

Pause, be still and know

The night draws in, the silence roars

There is a song, I know it well

There's a light that never fades

We are God's family

We choose to serve you

We're seeking

When we least expect it you arrive

FAMILY WORSHIP

With me, God is with me

GOD, LORD AND FATHER

Father in Heaven

There's beauty in this place

Who am I that the highest King

GOD'S LOVE AND FAITHFULNESS

Before I spoke a word, you were singing over me

God moves in a mysterious way

He sent his Son to die, and rise again to save us

I have this confidence because

Love at creation, love at the dawn

No height or depth can separate

Pause, be still and know

Standing in your love

The passion of our Saviour

There's a light that never fades

We are God's family

With me, God is with me

GUIDANCE AND DIRECTION

Christ be with me

Holy Spirit, guide my vision

With me, God is with me

You are the One who will provide

HEALING

How great the chasm that lay between us

It's time to dig a little deeper

New stories of wonders

Only you can make it right again

The rocks will cry out

HEART WORSHIP

Behold the King of kings

From the earth to the sky

I feel it in my bones, you're about to move

I have this confidence because

I love you Lord, oh your mercy never fails me

I saw the Lord

In the crushing

Made in perfect love

No height or depth can separate

Pause, be still and know

Praise the eternal, praise the immortal

See Jesus stripped of majesty

Stir a passion in my heart, God

The night draws in, the silence roars

There's a river flowing from the mountain

There's a light on the horizon

There's beauty in this place

When we least expect it you arrive

HEAVEN AND THE PROMISE OF ETERNITY

Holy Spirit, guide my vision

I saw the Lord

I was buried beneath my shame

Made in perfect love

See him there the great I am

There is a song, I know it well

There's a light that never fades

There's a river flowing from the mountain

We are God's family

You are the One who will provide

HOLY SPIRIT

Come like a fire

Fill this house with your glory

Holy Spirit, guide my vision

I feel it in my bones, you're about to move

It's time to dig a little deeper

New stories of wonders

Stir a passion in my heart, God

When we least expect it you arrive

JESUS - CROSS AND RESURRECTION

Love at creation, love at the dawn

On Calvary's hill, in morning light

See him there the great I am

See Jesus stripped of majesty

The greatest love song, the greatest story

The passion of our Saviour

There is a song, I know it well

You have shown me grace

JUSTICE

How good it is to sing

When our homes are hit by heartbreak

LOVE AND DEVOTION

Every eye in this place is on you now

Gathered in your name

I love you Lord, oh your mercy never fails me

I was buried beneath my shame

In the crushing

Only you can make it right again

Stir a passion in my heart, God

There's a river flowing from the mountain

You have shown me grace

MERCY, GRACE AND FORGIVENESS

Before I spoke a word, you were singing over me

For the things we've done and left undone

How good it is to sing

I love you Lord, oh your mercy never fails me

I was buried beneath my shame

Made in perfect love

No height or depth can separate

On Calvary's hill, in morning light

Standing in your love

The greatest love song, the greatest story

The passion of our Saviour

Too long I've been living with shame

Who am I that the highest King

You have shown me grace

MISSION

There's a light on the horizon

We choose to serve you

We're seeking

When our homes are hit by heartbreak

MYSTERY/ TRANSCENDENCE AND POWER OF GOD

Behold the King of kings

God moves in a mysterious way

How good it is to sing

It's time to dig a little deeper

Praise the eternal, praise the immortal

The rocks will cry out

When we least expect it you arrive

You have shown me grace

Your great love burns within our hearts

PRAISE AND THANKSGIVING

Every eye in this place is on you now

Gathered in your name

He sent his Son to die, and rise again to save us

He's the Lord of creation

Praise him you stars above

Praise the eternal, praise the immortal

See him there the great I am

The rocks will cry out

We are an altar of broken stones

You have shown me grace

PRAYER AND INTERCESSION

Christ be with me

Father in Heaven

Gathered in your name

I feel it in my bones, you're about to move

Made in perfect love

We're seeking

When our homes are hit by heartbreak

PROCLAMATION

Behold the King of kings

From the earth to the sky

Only you can make it right again

The rocks will cry out

Who am I that the highest King

You are the One who will provide

Your great love burns within our hearts

RENEWAL AND REFRESHMENT

Come like a fire

I feel it in my bones, you're about to move

Pause, be still and know

Standing in your love

Stir a passion in my heart, God

There's a river flowing from the mountain

RESPONSE

Be still and know

Come like a fire

Every eye in this place is on you now

Father in Heaven

Fill this house with your glory

For the things we've done and left undone

Holy Spirit, guide my vision

How great the chasm that lay between us

I love you Lord, oh your mercy never fails me

I saw the Lord

In the crushing

It's time to dig a little deeper

Only you can make it right again

See Jesus stripped of majesty

The night draws in, the silence roars

There's a river flowing from the mountain

There's a light on the horizon

There's beauty in this place

Too long I've been living with shame

We choose to serve you

When our homes are hit by heartbreak

When we least expect it you arrive

Who am I that the highest King

SPIRITUAL WARFARE

Behold the King of kings

I raise a hallelujah

It's time to dig a little deeper

New stories of wonders

The rocks will cry out

SUFFERING AND TRIALS

Be still and know

He sent his Son to die, and rise again to save us

How great the chasm that lay between us

I have this confidence because

I raise a hallelujah

In the crushing

Only you can make it right again

The night draws in, the silence roars

We are God's family

We're seeking

When our homes are hit by heartbreak

You are the One who will provide

Your great love burns within our hearts

SUITABLE FOR SOLO OR PRESENTATION

I was buried beneath my shame

Pause, be still and know

When we least expect it you arrive

TRINITY

Christ be with me

NOTES

NOTES

NOTES

NOTES